I Want to Be Like
Jesus

Written by L. J. Sattgast & Jan Elkins
Illustrated by Russ Flint

Zonderkidz
The Children's Group of Zondervan Publishing House

for Anna & David —JE

for Caleb & Allison —LJS

I Want to Be Like Jesus

Text Copyright ©1994 L. J. Sattgast & Jan Elkins
Illustrations ©1994 by Russ Flint

Requests for information should be addressed to:

Zonder**kidz**™
The Children's Group of Zondervan Publishing House
Grand Rapids, Michigan, 49530
www. zonderkidz.com

Zonderkidz is a trademark of the Zondervan Corporation

ISBN: 0-310-70102-3

I Want To Be Like Jesus was previously published as *Teach Me About Jesus* by Gold 'n' Honey, a division of Multnomah Publishers.

Printed in Singapore

00 01 02 03 04 /TW/ 5 4 3 2 1

Contents

A Note to Parents

Since young children are often familiar with many of the stories about Jesus, we have chosen instead to focus on the heart of His teaching so that children will come to know Him even better.

It is our belief that the principles Jesus taught are best learned while children are young and in the process of forming spiritual habits that will affect them for a lifetime.

L. J. Sattgast

BEING THANKFUL

Sometimes when I get up
the sun is shining.
I get dressed right away
and eat my favorite cereal
for breakfast. I say,
"Thank you Jesus
for such a nice day!"

The Lord has done it on this day.
Let us be joyful and glad in it.
PSALM 118:24

It's easy to be happy
when my dad plays a game
of hide and seek with me.
"Thank you, Jesus,
for such a great dad!"

Every good and perfect gift is from God.
It comes down from the Father.
He created the heavenly lights.
He does not change like shadows that move.
JAMES 1:17

But when Dad says,
"I have work to do,"
I can scowl and complain,
OR...
I can find something else to do.

Give thanks no matter what happens.
God wants you to thank him
because you believe in Christ Jesus.

1 THESSALONIANS 5:18

Most of the time I am nice
to my little brother.
I even let him play
with some of my toy cars.
"Thank you, Jesus,
for my family!"

———

Always give thanks to God the Father for everything.
Give thanks to him in the name of our Lord Jesus Christ.
EPHESIANS 5:20

13

But sometimes I am mean
to my brother. I push him away
and make him cry. When my mom
makes me sit in the corner,
I can grumble and pout,
OR...

I can say I was wrong.

"Dear Jesus, I'm sorry I was mean.

I'm glad You love me

just as much, even when I do

something wrong."

*What is love? It is not that we loved God.
It is that he loved us and sent his Son
to give his life to pay for our sins.*

1 John 4:10

Jesus is great and strong and kind.
Even when something bad happens,
Jesus can turn it into
something good.

---

*We know that in all things God works
for the good of those who love him.
He appointed them to be saved in
keeping with his purpose.*

ROMANS 8:28

19

Jesus has given me so much to enjoy.
I want to praise and thank Him
all day long—in everything I say
and everything I do!

FAITH

When Keiko's aunt came to visit
she brought her a present.
It was a shiny painted mirror
from Japan.

"Thank you!" said Keiko.
She smiled her brightest smile,
and the girl in the mirror
smiled back.

Keiko played a game
with her mirror.
She turned it this way and that.
"I see you, Mother!" she said.

She turned it again.

"I see you, Chester!"

Chester fluffed his feathers
and chirped.

"Mother, may I go next door
to show Lisa my new mirror?"
"Not right now,"
said Keiko's mother.
"It's almost time for dinner."

Keiko began to pout and whine.
"Look in your mirror,"
said Mother.

This is what Keiko saw.
The girl in the mirror
looked so silly.

Keiko started to laugh.
"I like that face much better,"
said Mother.

"Did you know *you* are like
a mirror?" asked Mother.

Keiko was surprised.
"How am I like a mirror?"

"Your face shows me
what you are looking at
or thinking about. Just now,
when something nice happened,
you had a happy face.
But what kind of face did you have
when you didn't get your way?"

"Jesus wants you to look at *Him* and believe what *He* says. Then He can change your heart to be more like Him."

"But I can't see Jesus," Keiko said.

Our faces are not covered with a veil.
We all display the Lord's glory.
We are being changed to become more like him
so that we have more and more glory.

2 Corinthians 3:18

"One way to look at Jesus,"
said Mother,
"is to read about Him
in the Bible."

*What I received I passed on to you. And it is the most
important of all. Here is what it is. Christ died for our sins,
just as Scripture said he would. He was buried.
He was raised from the dead on the third day,
just as Scripture said he would be.*

1 CORINTHIANS 15:3

"Another way to look at Jesus
is to ask yourself what Jesus
would want you to do."

Christ suffered for you. He left you an example.
He expects you to follow in his steps.
1 PETER 2:21

"What do people see
when they look at *you*?"
asked Mother.

Keiko thought for a moment.
Then she put down her mirror
and ran to the kitchen.

I want people to see
that I'm looking at Jesus!"
she said.

Let us keep looking to Jesus. He is the author of faith.
He also makes it perfect.

Hebrews 12:2

FORGIVENESS

Jordan wanted to plant a garden.
He had five packets of seed
and all the tools he needed.
He also had something
he *didn't* need…

A patch of ground full of rocks.

But Jordan planted his seeds
anyway.

Jordan's garden
did not grow very well.
"Looks like you need some help,"
said Grandpa.
Together they dug up the rocks
and threw them out one by one.

When the ground was ready
they planted and watered
the seeds.

Do you think
Jordan's garden grew?

Yes, it did!
There were enough flowers to
share with friends and neighbors.

Grandpa sat Jordan on his knee.
"There's another kind of rock
that needs to be thrown out,"
he said.

"What is it, Grandpa?"
asked Jordan.

"All our hurt feelings
are like rocks in a garden,"
Grandpa replied.
"Our feelings get hurt
when someone calls us stupid."

65

"Our feelings get hurt
when someone pushes us
and we fall down
and skin our knees."

"Our feelings get hurt
when it's our turn
and someone else gets to go first."

"How do I get rid of *those* kinds
of rocks, Grandpa?"
asked Jordan.

69

"Do you know what Jesus did
when He was hurt?
He said, 'I forgive you'
to the people who hurt Him.
When we forgive the people
who hurt us, it is like getting rid
of the rocks in our garden."

Men looked down on him. They didn't accept him.
He knew all about sorrow and suffering.
ISAIAH 53:3

"Then Jesus can grow
something good in *me*—
can't He, Grandpa?
asked Jordan.

"Yep," said Grandpa, "He can!"

———

Others received the seed that fell on good soil.
They are those who hear the message and understand it.
They produce a crop 100, 60 or 30 times more than the
farmer planted.
MATTHEW 13:23

WALKING IN THE LIGHT

(Confession and Repentance)

Gwendolyn wore her best dress
for Patsy's birthday party.
"Be careful with the present,"
said Mother. "And remember
to stay on the path."

Gwendolyn skipped along
until she saw raspberry bushes
on a hillside above the path.
How Gwendolyn loved raspberries!

I won't be long, thought Gwendolyn.
She ran quickly to the bushes
and began filling her mouth
with fat, juicy berries.

Just then, Gwendolyn heard
a noise in the thicket.
Was it a wild animal?

Gwendolyn tried to run,
but she tripped on a root.

It was only a friendly dog
coming to say hello.
"Ohhh!" wailed Gwendolyn.
"Look at the present!
And look at my clothes!"

At the party,
Patsy's mother put medicine
on Gwendolyn's scratches.
And she said she could mend
the broken teapot that Gwendolyn
had brought as a gift.

Everyone had a good time—
except for Gwendolyn.
What would she tell Mother
about her torn dress?

She could try to hide
what she had done.
Or she could tell her mother
what really happened,
and ask for forgiveness.

89

What would Jesus want Gwendolyn to tell her mother?

———

So admit to one another that you have sinned.
Pray for one another so that you might be healed.

JAMES 5:16

I'm so sorry, Mother.
I disobeyed and left the path
to pick raspberries.

When we tell Jesus
that we are disobeying,
He always forgives us.
Then we can walk
together in the light
and be best friends again!

If we admit that we have sinned,
he will forgive us our sins.
1 JOHN 1:9

My Book of Thanks

- Go through magazines and cut out pictures of things you are thankful for. If your child can't find a picture she wants, have her draw one. Even young children can do this, though they may have to tell you what it is when they are finished.
- Collect snapshots of family and friends whom you love and are thankful for.
- Glue the pictures and photos into a notebook. (You can make your own by folding sheets of blank paper in half and stapling them in the middle).
- Keep the notebook in a handy spot where your family can refer to it often.

Faith Mirror

- Out of cardboard, cut the shape of Keiko's mirror. (To make it sturdier, cut two mirror shapes and paste them together.)
- Let your child decorate the back of the "mirror."

Try these possibilities:
- Paint the entire surface with one color of poster paint before decorating.
- Cut petals and leaves out of construction paper and make flower designs.
- Cut out a variety of shapes and do an abstract design.
- Make a design with glue, then sprinkle with glitter.

Make a Forgiveness Rock

- For each family member, collect a rock about the size of a potato.
- Wash and dry the rocks, then paint them any way you wish—the more unique the better. (Poster paint works well.)
- When the paint is dry, write the word "Forgive" on the rock. Use a felt pen, or try fabric paint for a raised look.
- Decide together the best places to display the rocks— places where the rocks will most often remind your family to forgive.

Optional: To make a paperweight out of the rock, glue a piece of felt to the bottom. Use thick glue to make the felt stick.